Roman things to make and do

Leonie Pratt

Designed and illustrated by Vicky Arrowsmith

Additional design and illustrations by Sam Chandler,
Abigail Brown, Jessica Johnson and Antonia Miller
Steps and stickers illustrated by Molly Sage

Photographs by Howard Allman

Contents

Standing soldier paperchain

1. Fold a paper rectangle in half, then in half again. Draw a soldier's head and shoulders, then add a curve for the neck. Add a shield on one side, touching the fold.

2. Draw a spear. Then, add a hand holding the spear so that the arm is close to the fold, like this. Draw a shape for the soldier's tunic, then add the legs and feet.

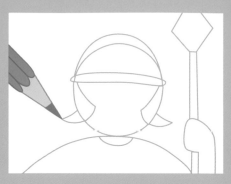

3. For the helmet, draw a rim across the head. Add a curve for the top, then draw two cheek guards overlapping the face. Draw curves on either side of the head.

The soldiers with feathers on their helmets are centurions. They also wore metal leg protectors.

Adding shapes to the plates makes them look as if they are overlapping.

Don't cut around the folds, marked here in red.

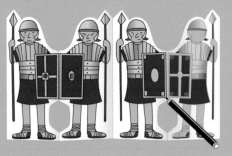

4. Draw a belt and some plates across the middle of the soldier's body. Then, add lines for shoulder plates. Draw shapes at the top of the plates, like this.

5. Keeping the paper folded, cut around the soldier through all the layers of paper. Take care not to cut the folds near the shield and spear. Unfold the paper.

6. Draw more Roman soldiers with shields and spears inside the other shapes. Fill them in using pencils. Then, use a black pen to draw outlines and faces.

The Romans' large and well-trained army allowed them to take over most of Europe and parts of Africa and Asia.

Racing chariot painting

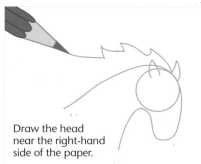

Draw the head near the right-hand side of the paper.

1. Draw a circle about the size of a big coin for a horse's cheek. Draw a curving nose, then add ears and a neck. Add the horse's mane along the neck.

2. Draw a long body. Then, add two curving legs coming out from the front of the body, and two coming out from the back. Draw a tail.

3. For another horse, draw a head in front of the first horse, then add the neck and body. Draw the legs slightly in front of the first horse's legs, then add a mane and tail.

You could paint two chariots racing against each other.

Chariots were pulled by a team of two or four horses around a huge oval arena called a circus. It was a fast and dangerous sport, as the chariots had open backs and the charioteers could fall off.

Draw the man's arms stretching forward.

The splatters will look like dust flicked up by the horses and chariot.

4. Draw a slanted oval for a wheel, then add a chariot above. Draw a man's head above the chariot, and add the body and arms. Then, draw the helmet.

5. Fill in everything using watery paints. Then, dip a dry brush in brown paint and hold it near the paper. Pull your finger over the bristles to splatter paint, like this.

6. When the paint is dry, use pencils to draw straps and bridles on the horses. Add patterns on the chariot and helmet, then draw around the wheel and add spokes.

Roman sword

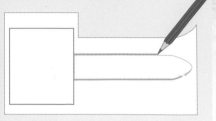
Lay the blade so that it comes out of the middle of the rectangle.

Pinching along the lines will make the sword 3-D.

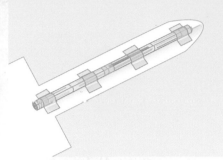

1. Draw a blade on a piece of thin cardboard, then cut it out. Draw a rectangle for a handle, then lay the blade next to it, like this, and draw around it.

2. Cut around the second shape. Pressing hard with a ballpoint pen, draw a line along the middle of each blade. Then, turn the blades over and pinch along the lines.

3. Cut a piece of newspaper as long as the blade. Roll the paper tightly and secure it with tape. Then, tape it inside one of the blades, a little way below the tip.

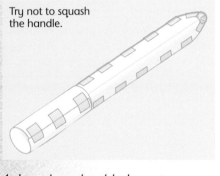
Try not to squash the handle.

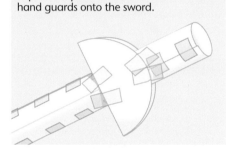
Tape the top and bottom of the hand guards onto the sword.

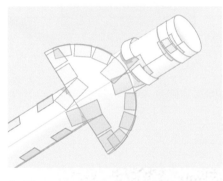

4. Lay the other blade on top so that the edges line up, then tape them together with sticky tape. Bend in the edges of the handle and tape them, too.

5. Draw around a big roll of sticky tape on cardboard and cut it out. Cut the circle in half to make two hand guards, then tape one onto each side of the sword.

6. Tape together the edges of the hand guards. Then, cut two thin cardboard strips and wrap them around the handle for grips. Secure them with sticky tape.

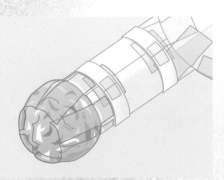

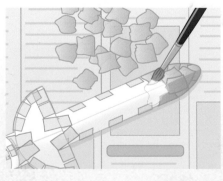

7. Cut a big square from kitchen foil, then tightly scrunch it into a ball. Push the ball into the end of the handle and use sticky tape to hold it in place.

8. Rip lots of pieces of silver tissue paper. Mix a little water with some white glue, then brush some onto the blade and press on pieces of silver paper.

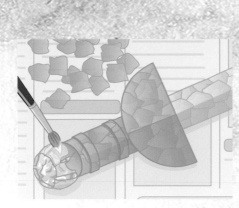

9. Brush on more glue and press on more paper until the blade is covered. Rip pieces of gold tissue paper, then glue them all over the hand guards and handle.

The dagger above was made in the same way as the sword, then decorated with gold pen.

A Roman soldier's short sword was called a gladius. This kind of sword was used for stabbing and slashing at enemy soldiers.

A soldier's shield covered his body and the tops of his legs. It was made with lightweight wood so it wasn't heavy to carry.

Look at the shields on this page for different ways to decorate a shield.

Soldier's shield

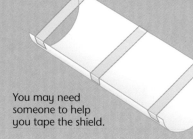

You may need someone to help you tape the shield.

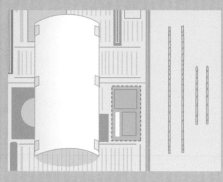

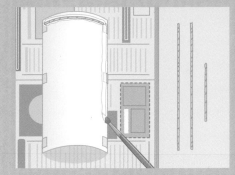

1. Cut a very big rectangle for a shield from thin cardboard. Bend the long sides around to make the shield curved. Then, tape the sides so the shield stays curved.

2. Lay the shield with the curved side up on some newspaper. Cut four pieces of string, two almost as wide as the shield, and two almost as long.

3. Brush a line of glue near one short side of the shield and press on one of the short pieces of string. Glue on the rest of the string around the other edges.

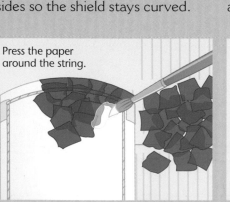

Press the paper around the string.

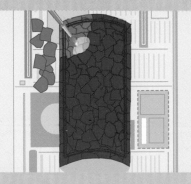

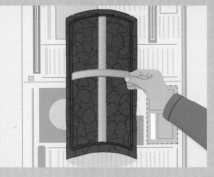

4. Mix a little water with white glue in an old container. Then, rip up lots of pieces of tissue paper. Brush part of the shield with the glue and press on pieces of paper.

5. Brush on more glue and press on more paper until the shield is covered with two layers of paper. Brush on one more layer of glue, then leave the shield to dry.

6. Cut a long strip from gold paper or cardboard and glue it down the middle of the shield. Cut another shorter strip and glue it across the middle.

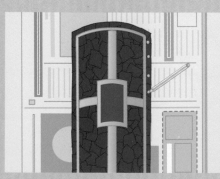

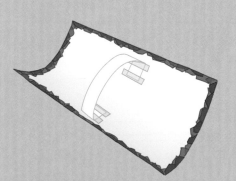

7. Cut a gold and a red rectangle and glue them in the middle of the shield. Then, brush gold paint along the string border. Use a gold pen to draw studs, too.

8. Cut off the tape, then cut a cardboard strip as wide as the shield. Fold under the ends and lay the strip across the middle of the shield. Tape the ends down.

9. Cut another strip that is half as wide as the first one and tape it near the top of the shield. Put your arm up through the big strip and hold the small one, like this.

City collage

1. Cut two rectangles from pale tissue paper for an aqueduct and a stadium. Mix a little water into some white glue and glue the shapes onto a piece of paper.

2. Cut out smaller shapes from tissue paper to make buildings and steps. Glue them onto the paper, along the bottom of the aqueduct and stadium.

3. Cut out shapes for roofs, and strips for columns. Then, cut out some little rectangles for windows. Glue the windows, roofs and columns onto the buildings.

Aqueducts were like giant water pipes that carried fresh water from nearby mountains into the city for everyone to use.
People went to a stadium to watch gladiators fight. The building was circular, with rows of stone seats around the edge and an arena in the middle.

4. Cut out some curved shapes to go on the aqueduct. Make arched doorways by cutting out some bigger arches and folding them in half, then cutting out the middle.

5. Glue on all the doorways. Add small curved shapes near the top of the aqueduct and larger ones below. Then, brush a thin layer of glue all over the picture.

6. When the glue is dry, use a thin black pen to draw outlines and details on the smaller buildings. Then, add details to the aqueduct and stadium, too.

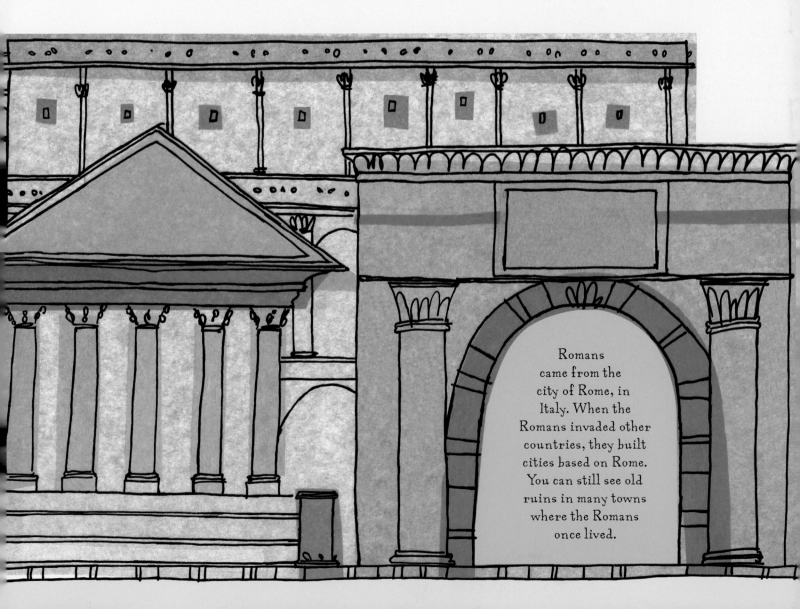

Romans came from the city of Rome, in Italy. When the Romans invaded other countries, they built cities based on Rome. You can still see old ruins in many towns where the Romans once lived.

Gladiator fight

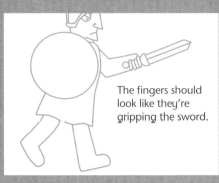

The fingers should look like they're gripping the sword.

1. Draw a gladiator's helmet near the top of a piece of thick white paper. Draw a long nose, then add the gladiator's eye, mouth, chin and neck.

2. Draw a circle for a shield, then add the body and legs. Draw one arm reaching forward. Then, draw small sausage shapes for the fingers and add a sword.

3. Add sandals and details on the clothes. Fill everything in using felt-tip pens, then draw over the outlines with a black pen. Cut out the gladiator, leaving a thin border.

Make the gladiator 'fight' the lion by holding the handles and sliding them toward each other.

Gladiators were prisoners or slaves who were made to fight each other, or wild animals, to the death. Lots of people, including the emperor, came to watch these gruesome battles and cheer on the gladiator they liked best.

Glue each handle in the middle.

4. Draw a lion's snout facing the other way from the gladiator. Add a snarling mouth, then draw a mane around the top of the head. Add an eye and an ear.

5. Add the lion's front legs. Then, draw the body, and add back legs and a tail. Use felt-tip pens to fill in the lion, then cut it out, leaving a small border.

6. Cut two strips for handles from thick paper. Fold over one end of each handle, then glue one handle onto the back of the lion and one onto the back of the gladiator.

You could make another gladiator to fight with, instead of a lion.

7. Cut a curved shape for an arena from pale paper. Glue the arena onto a big piece of cardboard. Then, cut another long strip from pale paper and fold under the ends.

Hook the gladiator and the lion over the strip.

8. Glue the ends of the strip onto the background, a little way up from the bottom. Then, slide the handles of the gladiator and lion under the strip.

Scroll

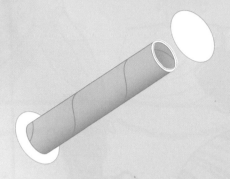

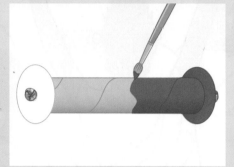

You could tie the scroll with a ribbon.

1. Lay a cup on thin cardboard and draw around it twice. Cut out the circles. Brush glue on the ends of a cardboard tube from a paper towel roll, then press on the circles.

2. Cut two small pieces of tissue paper. Dip them in glue, then roll each one into a ball. Press the balls onto the ends of the scroll. Let the glue dry, then paint the scroll.

3. When the paint is dry, cut a rectangle of paper that is nearly as wide as the cardboard tube. Tape the paper on and wrap it around the scroll.

I = 1   **II** = 2   **III** = 3   **IV** = 4

V = 5   **VI** = 6   **VII** = 7   **VIII** = 8

IX = 9   **X** = 10   **XI** = 11   **XII** = 12

L = 50   **C** = 100   **D** = 500   **M** = 1,000

The symbols on this scroll are Roman numerals. Romans used these in the same way we use numbers today.

Romans wrote things on scrolls instead of books. A scroll was kept rolled up until someone wanted to read what was on it.

Emperor's wreath

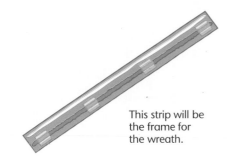

This strip will be the frame for the wreath.

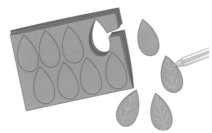

This will make 32 leaves.

1. Cut a paper rectangle that is a little longer than a pipe cleaner. Tape a pipe cleaner along the middle, then fold the paper in half. Glue the edges together.

2. Fold a piece of green paper in half, then in half again. Draw eight leaves on the paper, then cut them out through all the layers. Draw veins on each leaf with a gold pen.

3. Bend the frame into a curve that fits around the top of your head. Then, glue one leaf onto each end of the frame. This will be the front of the wreath.

Glue the pairs a little way behind the first leaves.

4. Pair the leaves up, then glue each pair together to make a 'V' shape. Then, glue two pairs of leaves onto the frame, one onto each side.

5. Add more pairs of leaves, two at a time, on either side of the frame. Where the leaves meet in the middle, glue one pair facing up, like this. Let the glue dry.

Roman emperors wore wreaths like these made from laurel leaves. This showed everyone how important they were, because laurel leaves were a symbol of power or victory.

The frame of this wreath was made using gold paper.

Pop-up Roman god card

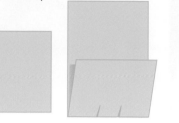

Put the square to the side until step 4.

1. Cut a rectangle and square that are the same width from blue cardboard. Fold up the bottom third of the rectangle. Then, make two cuts into the fold for a flap.

2. Fold the flap to the front and to the back. Then, unfold the card and push the flap through to the inside, like this. Close the card and press it flat.

3. Open the card and lay it flat. Fold up the bottom edge so that it touches the fold. Then, use a silver pen to draw waves on the folded part and above the flap.

Neptune was the Roman god of the sea.

Diana was Jupiter's daughter. She was the goddess of hunting and the moon.

This moon was cut from silver paper, then glued onto the back part of the card.

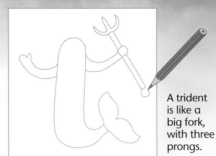

A trident is like a big fork, with three prongs.

4. Draw waves on the square from step 1. Then, cut along the top of the waves on the square. Cut along the top of the card, and along the folded part, at the front.

5. Draw a shape for Neptune's head, body and tail on thick paper. Add fins on the end of the tail, then draw two arms, with one holding a trident.

6. Draw a long nose and dots for eyes, then draw hair and a long beard. Add a crown and draw fins under the arms and scales on the tail. Erase any overlapping lines.

Jupiter was the ruler of the gods.

Romans believed in many different gods and goddesses.

7. Fill everything in using felt-tip pens. Then, go over the lines with a thin black pen. Cut out the shape, then glue Neptune onto the square from step 4.

8. Open the card so that the tallest waves are at the back. Glue the square onto the front of the flap, then fold up the waves at the front again.

Coins and money bags

Silver coins

Roman coins aren't perfectly round like modern coins.

1. Fold a piece of thin cardboard in half. Draw an uneven circle for a coin, so that part of the edge touches the fold. Cut out the shape through both layers.

2. Open out the shape and glue it onto a piece of kitchen foil. Cut around the shape, leaving a small border, then fold the foil over the edge, all the way around.

You could use gold foil from a chocolate wrapper to make gold coins like these ones.

You could draw a Roman emperor on one side of your coin.

Roman coins were made from copper, bronze, silver or gold. A picture of the emperor was stamped on one side of each coin, to show who was ruling the Roman Empire.

3. Spread glue on the cardboard and press the two halves together until they stick. Then, use a blunt pencil to draw pictures on both sides of the coin.

Money bags

Don't glue
this edge.

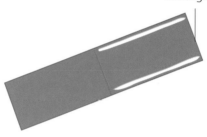

1. For a money bag, cut a long rectangle from felt. Fold it in half, mark where the fold is, then unfold it. Spread white glue along the edges of one half, to the mark.

You could push a sharp pencil through the felt instead of using a hole puncher.

2. Carefully fold over the other side of the rectangle so that the edges line up, to make a bag. Press the edges together, then leave the glue to dry.

3. Use one side of a hole puncher to make a hole near one edge of the bag. Make the hole a little way down from the open end. Do the same on the other side.

4. Thread a long piece of string or ribbon through the hole on one side of the bag, then back through the other. Put coins in the bag and tie the ends of the string.

Printed mosaics

A mosaic is a name for a picture or pattern made from lots of small squares. The floors of Roman houses were often decorated with mosaics. Tiny square tiles were pressed into wet plaster. When the plaster dried, it held the tiles in place.

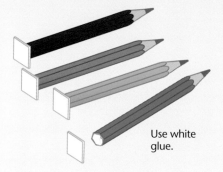

Use white glue.

1. Cut out a rectangle that is at least 18cm x 14cm (7in x 5½in) from thick paper or cardboard. Draw a very simple picture in the middle of the rectangle.

2. Draw a border a little way in from the edges of the rectangle. Then, add a simple background around the picture in the middle, such as clouds or grass.

3. To make stamps for printing, cut four squares from stiff cardboard that are a little bigger than the end of a pencil. Glue the squares onto four old pencils.

You could use the ideas on these pages to make different mosaics.

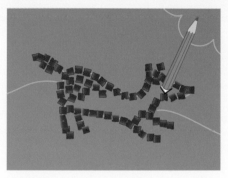

Print around the outside edge of
something before filling it in.

4. Lay a sponge cloth on some
newspaper. Then, spread four
blobs of paint onto the sponge
cloth. Press one of the stamps
into the paint.

5. Press the stamp onto the paper
to make a print. Print around the
outline of the picture, then fill it in,
pressing the stamp into the paint
after every few prints.

6. Fill in the background and the
border, using a different stamp
for each paint. When the paint is
dry, erase any pencil lines from
steps 1 and 2.

The mosaics on this page are
shown smaller than full size.

Catapult

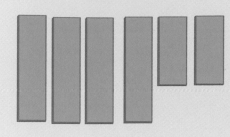

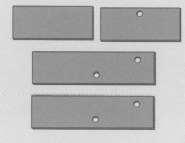

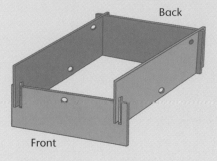

Back

Front

1. Cut four strips about 15cm (6in) long from thick cardboard. Then, cut two slightly shorter strips that are the same width. Put two of the long strips to the side until step 5.

2. Use a hole puncher to make holes in three of the strips, like this. Make sure that the holes in the long strips are in the same place on each strip.

3. Make two cuts halfway down into each short strip, near the end. Then, make two cuts up into the ends of the long strips. Slot the strips together in a rectangle.

Use a pencil to make the holes bigger if you need to.

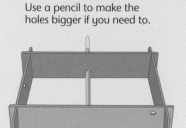

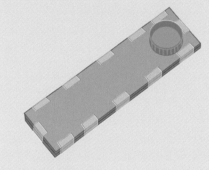

Make one set of cuts above where the arm rests on the base, and one below.

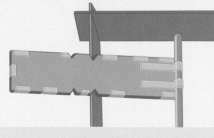

4. Cut a straw so it is a little wider than the base. Push it through the holes in the middle of the long sides, then slide a pipe cleaner in and twist the ends.

5. To make the arm, lay the two long strips from step 1 on top of each other and tape them together. Glue a clean bottle top near one end of the arm.

6. With the lid at the top and facing the front, tape the arm onto the straw. Rest the arm on the front of the base and make four cuts, two on either side of the arm.

The rubber band rests in the bottom cuts.

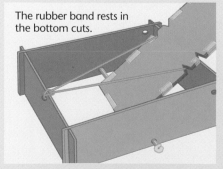

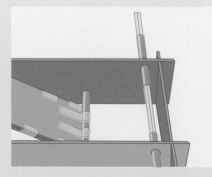

Pull the rubber band so that it can't move on the satay stick.

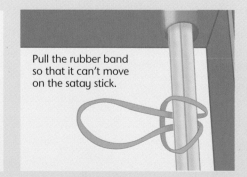

7. Push a rubber band that is 9cm (3½in) long through the hole in the front of the base to make a loop. Pull the end of the band through the loop and hook it onto the arm.

8. Cut two pieces from a straw and push the pieces through the holes at the back of the base. Then, slide two satay or kebab sticks through the straws.

9. Loop another rubber band around the satay sticks. Push one end through the loop and pull it very tight. Hook it over the top cuts in the arm.

Roman soldiers sometimes surrounded an enemy town, so that no one could get in or out. They used catapults to throw huge rocks over the town walls.

To fire the catapult, twist the satay sticks so that the rubber band pulls the arm back. Without letting go of the sticks, put a foil ball in the lid. Then...

...hold the base and let go of the sticks to fire the ball.

You could draw planks on the cardboard in step 1, to make it look like wood.

25

Cuffs and bangles
Cuff

This red cuff had string glued onto it in step 1 (see the shield on page 9).

You could use stickers from the middle of this book to decorate a cuff.

Brush an extra layer of glue after you have completely covered each cuff.

1. Cut two cardboard rectangles that fit tightly around your wrists. Take off the cuffs, then cut the corners to make them rounded. Tape each cuff so it stays curved.

2. Rip up pieces of tissue paper. Mix a little water with white glue in an old container, then brush glue on the cuffs. Press on the tissue paper to cover the cuffs.

3. When the glue is dry, cut along the tape. Make holes in shiny paper with a hole puncher, then empty the puncher and glue the circles onto the cuffs for studs.

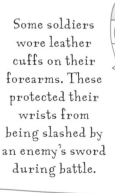

Some soldiers wore leather cuffs on their forearms. These protected their wrists from being slashed by an enemy's sword during battle.

4. To put on a cuff, open your hand flat and slide the open part of the cuff onto your hand. Then, slide the cuff down onto your wrist and twist it around.

Bangle

Spread glue here.

1. For a bangle, cut a gold paper rectangle that is a little longer than a pipe cleaner. Tape a pipe cleaner along the middle. Fold the paper in half and glue the edges.

2. Fold a piece of gold paper in half so that the gold sides face out. Glue the halves together. Draw a circle and a snake's head on the paper, then cut them out.

3. Glue the head onto one end of the gold strip and the circle onto the other end. Cut out eyes from shiny paper and a small circle for the end. Glue them on.

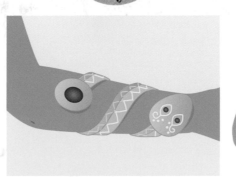

4. Use a silver pen to draw around the eyes. Draw a pattern along the strip, too. Then, bend the strip so that the snake spirals around your arm, like this.

Roman women wore bangles around their wrists or above their elbows.

You could use stickers from the middle of this book to decorate the ends of your bangle.

27

Roman feast picture

Glue the couches along the sides and bottom of the table.

1. Cut four rectangles for a table and couches from different papers. Cut the corners off the couches to make them rounded, then glue everything onto a piece of paper.

2. Draw circles and ovals on the table for plates. Add cups and jugs in between the plates. Then, draw food such as fruit, fish and meat on the plates.

3. For a dinner guest leaning on a couch, draw the head. Then, draw one arm slanting down, with the hand out. Add a curved body, legs and bare feet.

Draw the guest lying in the middle of the couch.

4. Draw another arm and add a hand as if it is gripping something. Then, draw the top of a cup above the hand and the base below, like this.

Draw details on the guests' clothes.

5. Draw more guests lying on the couches and add plates of food next to some of them. Cut out some shapes for cushions and glue them on, too.

Draw the top half of a guest's body at the edge of the table.

You could add bones and crumbs that have fallen off the guests' plates.

6. Use pencils to fill in the food and dinner guests. Then, draw patterns on the cushions. Outline the food and guests using a thin black pen.

Wealthy Romans liked having big feasts to show how rich they were. Guests had their feet and hands washed by slaves, then lay on couches around a table. Slaves brought plate after plate of food and everyone ate lying down. A really big feast could have up to seven courses and last ten hours.

Actors' masks

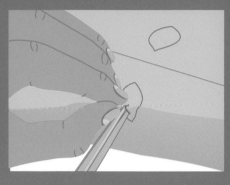

1. Fold a piece of thin cardboard in half, then open it out. Then, lay a pair of glasses on the cardboard so that the middle is over the fold. Draw around them.

2. Draw two eye holes, then erase the shape of the sunglasses. Pinch inside one eye hole and snip into the pinch. Then, cut out the eye. Do the same for the other eye.

3. Fold the cardboard in half again and draw half a head and half a mouth against the fold. With the cardboard folded, cut out the mouth, then cut around the head.

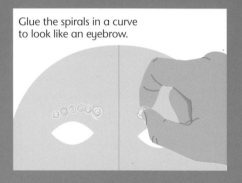

Glue the spirals in a curve to look like an eyebrow.

4. Cut 12 thin strips from pale paper. Fold over one end of each strip, then tightly roll them into spirals. Dip the spirals in glue and press them above the eyes.

5. Cut another thin strip. Bend it into a nose shape, then curl in one end for a nostril. Brush glue along the edge of the strip and press it onto the mask.

6. For the beard and hair, cut lots of strips from brown papers. Curl some strips into 'S' shapes by rolling one half into a spiral, then rolling in the other end, like this.

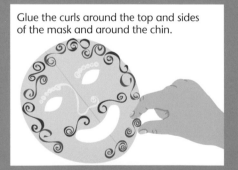

Glue the curls around the top and sides of the mask and around the chin.

7. Glue one 'S' shape above the mouth, then glue another 'S' shape on, going the other way, like this. Add more curls around the edge of the mask.

8. Roll some strips into tight spirals and some into slightly uncurled spirals. Then, glue all the spirals onto the mask in between the gaps in the curls.

9. Turn the mask over. Then, cut two long pieces of ribbon and tape one onto either side of the mask. You can put the mask on and tie the ribbons around your head.

In Ancient Rome, only men were allowed to act on stage, so female roles were actually played by men. The actors wore bright masks so that it was easy for the audience to tell who the characters were.

You could make a mask of a woman, with curls piled high on her head.

31

How to wear a toga

Wear a belt underneath your toga.

1. Fold a single bed sheet in half, along its length. Hold one long edge behind you at shoulder height. Then, flip one corner forward, over your left shoulder.

2. Hold the other corner in your right hand. Bring the material underneath your right arm and all the way across the front of your body.

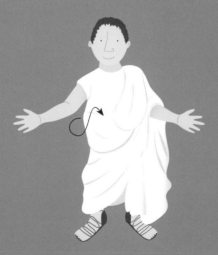

3. Flip the material in your right hand over your left shoulder. You may need to pull the sheet around a little bit, to keep your chest covered.

4. Pull the material around your back and under your right arm. Tuck the end of the material into the front of your toga, then into your belt.

Photographic manipulation: Nick Wakeford
This edition first published in 2012 by Usborne Publishing Ltd., Usborne House, 83-85 Saffron Hill, London, England. www.usborne.com